Colours and Shapes

Jane Hartzig

Illustrations by Jim Hansen

INDEX

Published by Arcturus Publishing Limited
for Index Books Limited
Henson Way, Kettering, Northamptonshire NN16 8PX

This edition published 2002

Copyright © Arcturus Publishing Limited
1–7 Shand Street, London SE1 2ES

ISBN 1-84193-091-1

Printed and bound in China

AUTHOR Jane Hartzig
ILLUSTRATOR Jim Hansen
EDITOR Rebecca Panayiotou
DESIGNER Alex Ingr
SERIES CONSULTANT Maureen Robinson

Introduction

Colours and Shapes is a beautifully illustrated and stimulating introduction to these areas for both pre-school children and those just starting their formal education.

How to use this book

☞ Don't attempt to finish the whole book in one session! Each child is an individual and will have a different concentration span.

☞ Children learn through play at this age, so make working on this book a fun thing to do, not a chore that has to be completed. One or two pages at a time is an achievable goal.

☞ Help your child by reading the instructions for them and explaining what is required in the exercises. If they have difficulty with any of the tasks you can help them.

☞ Each time your child has completed a page of this book, give them lots of praise and encouragement. Increase their sense of achievement by awarding them a star.

☞ Children are naturally inquisitive about the world around them, and love to share any new-found knowledge. So help them learn, praise their efforts, but most of all have fun!

green
white
yellow
pink
brown
orange
red
purple

Red is a primary colour

Red is the colour of:

Apples on a tree.

Sweets for you and me.

A red balloon – what a treat!

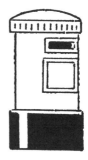

The post box at the end of your street.

Colour them all in red

Can you help Red Riding Hood get to Granny's house?

How many red things will she pass on the way?

Well done! Award yourself a star!

Yellow is a primary colour

Yellow is the colour of:

The stripes on a honey bee.

The sun, very warm on me!

A buttercup, growing in the spring.

A canary – listen to it sing!

Colour them all in yellow.

Tom is getting ready to go to the seaside – but he will only take yellow things with him!

Draw a circle round all the things Tom will put in his bucket. Finish colouring the bucket!

Well done! Award yourself a star!

Parent tip   Try helping your child to point out all the red and yellow items in the room. On the way to the shops or nursery school, encourage your child to be aware of colour. You could play a game and offer one point for noticing anything red (cars, buses etc) and two points for spotting something yellow.

Blue is the colour of:

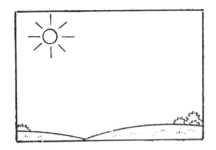

A summer sky.

A kite so high.

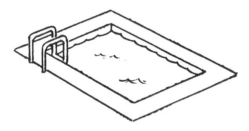

A swimming pool.

My bike – it's cool!

You can use light blue and **dark blue** to colour them in!

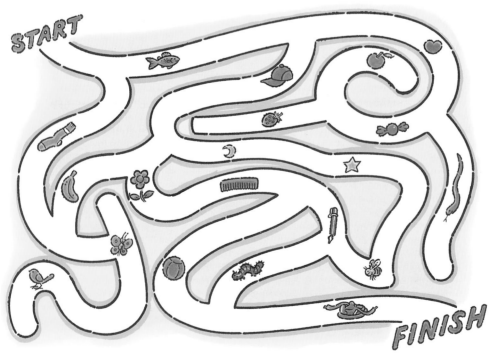

Use your finger to complete the maze – but only pass the blue things!

Well done! Award yourself a star!

Red and Yellow together make Orange

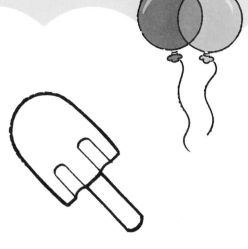

Orange is the colour of:

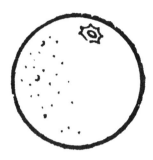

Orange fruit for you to pick.

A lollipop for you to lick!

The middle of a daffodil,
waving gently on a hill.

A bright orange jacket
so I am seen in the traffic!

Colour them all in orange. Can **you** make orange?

How many
orange things
can you see in
the picture?

Put your answer
in the box.

Well done! Award
yourself a star!

 *Encourage your child's observational skills by challenging him/her to find
various shades of blue or orange. Areas to examine might be curtains,
patterned crockery, carpets and clothes.*

Blue and Yellow together make **Green**

Green is the colour of:

A plateful of peas.

A forest of trees.

I put my gloves on –
I really love them!

Ten green bottles standing tall.
Watch out, watch out
or they might fall.

Colour them all in **green**. Can **you** make green?

Amy has hidden
ten green bottles
in the shed.
Can you find all
ten of them?

Well done! Award
yourself a star!

Red and Green together make Brown

Brown is the colour of:

The old trunk of a big oak tree.

A cow's big eyes for her to see.

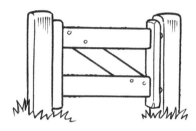

A gate to the field where we can play.

"Woof! Can we go?"
our dog will say.

Colour them all in **brown**. Can **you** make brown?

Can you match the animals to their homes? Which animal is NOT brown?

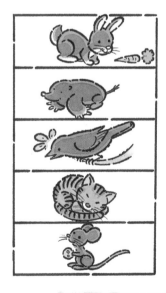

Parent tip *Your child may enjoy making a leaf collage. When in the garden or the park, collect a variety of leaves that have fallen from trees or bushes. Take these home and stick them to paper, creating a pattern. Talk to your child about the colours in the picture he/she has made. Even in spring, the leaves contain several colours.*

Red and Blue together make Purple

Purple is the colour of:

Pansies and violets in a vase.

An alien – is he from Mars?

A towel wrapped around my tummy.

Grapes in a bunch – very yummy!

Colour them all in **purple**. Can **you** make purple?

Here is Freddy, the friendly alien.

Only one of the space helmets will fit him. Find the right space helmet for Freddy's head and put a ring around it!

Well done! Award yourself a star!

Parent tip *Help your child to learn the colours of the rainbow: red, orange, yellow, green, blue, indigo and violet. It may help them if they are taught a rhyme as a means of remembering the colours. For example, "**Richard of York gave battle in vain**."*

Black

Black is the colour of:

A witch's hat – she looks quite mean.

A wizard's cloak, so he can't be seen.

Blackbirds flying very high.

Look up at the dark night sky.

Colour them all in **black**.

Wanda the witch is making a spell, but she only wants to put black things in her cauldron. Circle the things that Wanda will put in.

Well done! Award yourself a star!

11

White

Finish the man who is made of snow.

Draw some snowballs – for you to throw!

Here is a clean piece of paper – write your name on it!

Put buttons on the shirt – to finish it!

Here is a snow scene. Can you spot the things that are out of place? There are four things.

Well done! Award yourself a star!

Parent tip *Look in the food cupboard for white things to eat. Things to look out for are rice, bread, sugar etc. If you are feeling adventurous, perhaps you and your child could do some cooking with white ingredients.*

Red and White together make Pink

Pink is the colour of:

Pretty flowers in a bunch.   Strawberry ice cream to have after lunch!

A beautiful dress for me to wear.   A lovely cushion I bought at the fair!

Colour them all in pink. Can **you** make pink?

Which pink flamingo finds the way to the lake? Trace their paths with your finger to find out.

Well done! Award yourself a star!

Black and White together make Grey

Grey is the colour of:

Clouds when it's a rainy day.

Squirrels coming out to play.

A donkey, slowly chewing his tea.

An elephant, bigger than you or me!

Colour them all in grey. Can **you** make grey?

Here are lots of boys dressed in grey. Look at them carefully.

Only two are dressed exactly the same!
Circle the two boys wearing the same clothes.

Well done! Award
yourself a star!

Colour revision: colour by number

Colour in the painting, using the key. Have fun!

1. red
2. yellow
3. blue
4. orange
5. green
6. purple
7. brown
8. black
9. white
10. pink
11. grey

 Parent tip
Painting and drawing are excellent mediums for exploring colour. Encourage mixing colours and the use of lots of different colours in artwork.

Square

A square is a shape with four sides of the same length, and four equal corners.

Follow the lines to draw a square.

Can you draw a square?

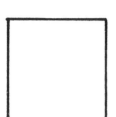

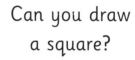

Billy is building a beautiful tower made of square bricks. Can you finish it for him?

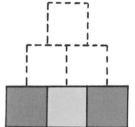

Finish the train.
Where do you think it's going?

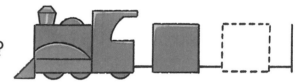

Spot the squares!

How many squares can you find in the picture? Is there anything wrong in the picture?

There are ☐ squares.

Well done! Award yourself a star!

16

Triangle

A triangle is a shape with three sides and three corners.

Follow the lines to draw a triangle.

Can you draw a triangle?

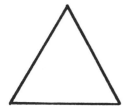

The fish love their fish food!

Finish drawing the fishes. Make their fins and tails by drawing triangles.

Colour the fish food in bright colours.

Pussycat, pussycat, where have you been?
I've been to London to look at the Queen.
Pussycat, pussycat, what did you there?
I frightened a little mouse under a chair!

Finish the queen's crown.

Finish drawing the cat's ears and nose.

How many pieces of cheese can you find in the picture?

Well done! Award yourself a star!

Parent tip   *Try drawing a robot using a variety of different sized squares and triangles for the body parts: eyes, nose, fingers etc. Let a younger/less confident child draw over the lines you draw as a way of developing pencil control.*

Circle

A circle is a perfectly round shape.

Follow the lines to draw a circle.

Can you draw a circle?

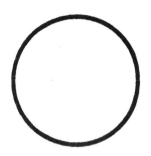 

Draw the snowman's round head, and give him some more buttons.

Draw round the dotted lines to finish the face!

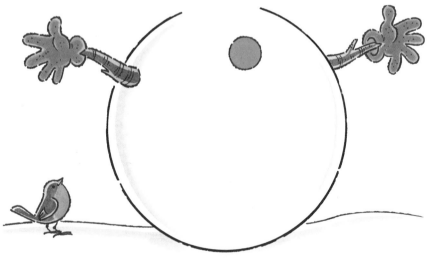

It SNOW problem!

Well done! Award yourself a star!

Rectangle

A rectangle is a shape with two long straight sides and two shorter straight sides. It has four equal corners.

Follow the lines to draw a rectangle.

Can you draw a rectangle?

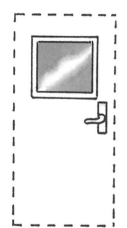

Follow the dotted lines to finish the door.
Colour it in the same colour as your own front door.

Knock, knock!
Who's there?
Atish.
Atish who?
Bless you!

Wee Willie Winkie
Runs through the town,
Upstairs and downstairs
In his nightgown.
Knocking at the windows,
Crying through the lock,
"Are the children all in bed
For it's past eight o'clock!"

How many rectangles can you spot in the picture?

 Parent tip *Why not make a pizza funny face! Take a plain pizza and add some circular tomato slices for the eyes. Then cut out some rectangles of carrot or courgette for the nose and mouth. You could even use some tinned sweetcorn for eyebrows and teeth.*

Well done! Award yourself a star!

★

Pentagon

A pentagon is a shape with five sides and five corners.

Follow the lines to draw a pentagon.

Can you draw a pentagon?

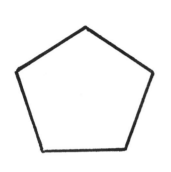

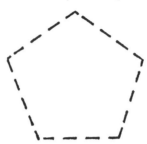

Finish all the flowers by drawing round the pentagon shapes in the middle of them.

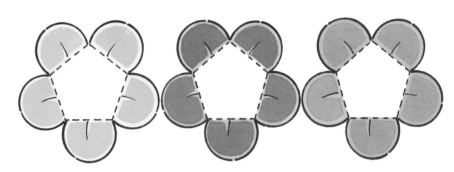

Colour them in bright colours!

Ben's shirt has lots of shapes on it! How many pentagons can you see?

Write the answer in the box.

Oval

An oval is a shape like a stretched-out circle. Eggs are oval.

Follow the lines to draw an oval.

Can you draw an oval?

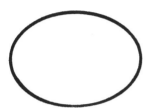

Mirror, mirror on the wall...

Finish the oval mirror, then draw your face in it. Try to make your face an oval too.

Finish drawing the hen's eggs.

eggs-actly right!

Humpty Dumpty sat on a wall,
Humpty Dumpty had a great fall,
All the King's horses and all the King's men
Couldn't put Humpty together again!

Draw in Humpty's eyes, nose and mouth.
Make them all ovals.
How many eggs can you see in the picture?

Well done! Award yourself a star!

★

Star

A star is a shape with straight lines and five or six points.

Here are two ways to draw a star. Start at the dots and follow the arrows.

Can you draw some stars?

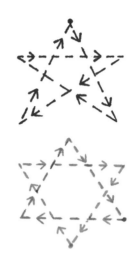

Twinkle, twinkle little star
How I wonder what you are.
Up above the world so high
Like a diamond in the sky.
Twinkle, twinkle little star
How I wonder what you are.

Draw some stars in the sky.

You're a star!

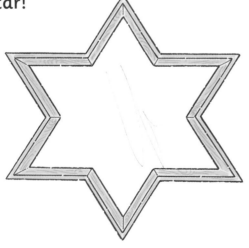

Draw your favourite toy, or person, or yourself in the star. Colour your picture in. Then, if you want to, you can cut it out and put it on your bedroom wall!

Well done! Award yourself a star!

Parent tip 👉 *Make a star stained glass ornament for your child's bedroom. Help your child to draw a large star on a piece of tracing paper, then colour it in with lots of bright colours. Now help your child to cut it out, stick it to the window, and watch the light shine through it!*

Shapes revision: Clarence the Clown

Clarence the clown is made of lots of different shapes. Can you find them all? Count them, and write the number of each of the shapes in the empty boxes.

Well done! Award yourself a star!

Shapes revision: Draw a House!

Let's draw a house! Look at the pictures below, follow the instructions and draw your own house in the space.

1) Start by drawing a square for the main part of the house.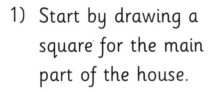

2) Then draw a triangle for the roof.

3) Now draw a rectangle for the door.

4) Finally, add some more squares and circles for the windows.

Now draw your house in the space below! Don't forget to colour it in!

Well done! Award yourself a star!